THE MACMILLAN COMPANY
NEW YORK · BOSTON · CHICAGO
DALLAS · ATLANTA · SAN FRANCISCO

MACMILLAN AND CO., LIMITED
LONDON · BOMBAY · CALCUTTA
MADRAS · MELBOURNE

THE MACMILLAN COMPANY
OF CANADA, LIMITED
TORONTO

THE NEW PROMETHEUS

By

LYMAN BRYSON

Professor of Education
Teachers College, Columbia University

NEW YORK
THE MACMILLAN COMPANY
1941

CONTENTS

EDITORIAL INTRODUCTION

The thirteenth volume in the Kappa Delta Pi Lecture Series accents anew, under the title *The New Prometheus* by Professor Lyman Bryson of Teachers College, Columbia University, the pressing and elusive problem of teaching mass-man to think, and to think straight. Professor Bryson is a widely known leader in adult education. His forums on the air have been a significant contribution to many-sided discussions of timely topics. In the present volume he forcefully and frankly probes into conditions that enchain the popular mind. His essay is concerned with ways and means of training young and old to appreciate and to use the *method* of scientific thinking, which means "how to use the methods by which rational intelligence works."

Appearances to the contrary not withstanding, the man in the street wants more knowledge because he is now aware of how much there is to know. From popular magazines, the radio, the moving picture, comes a steady torrent of information about a world which quickens curiosity and wonder. It is through knowledge and knowledge checked by critical intelligence that man gains power over his environment, enjoys a larger share in general understanding, becomes less fearful of nature, less provincial, and grows in ability to judge the worth of his experiences. While all of these objectives, in one form or another, have long directed educational efforts, it remains a fact that knowledge today is largely esoteric and cloistral and academic, withheld from the masses by complacent scholars who sneer at popularizations. In our own democracy knowledge is undemocratic. Intellect holds itself aloof from intelligence and would deny the ancient Greek conception of good as related to utility. So far as the common noncollegiate man is concerned, knowledge, the fire that empowers, is chained as was Prometheus of old. And like him the gods of the campus enchain the scholar who ventures to bring the fire of knowledge to the nonintellectuals. There is rich food for reflection in this essay by a servant of adult education. It is well to heed what he says about the need of making books more readable and more available. In this hour of rapid encroachments upon academic freedom of inquiry one should ponder upon the possibility that the vast stores of culture evolved by man over two thousand years may in America, as overseas, be destroyed by a barbarism that exalts race and blood and power, and enslaves freedom of body and mind. It is at this point that the method of science plays its constructive role: to subject to cautious scrutiny all claims by those who seek authoritarian control. Such control waxes fat upon a people's general ignorance. In order to be free one must be vigilant; vigilance depends upon the will and the ability to inquire.

Kappa Delta Pi, as an Honor Society in Education, finds pleasure in presenting Professor Bryson's stirring message to educators and laymen alike.

Alfred L. Hall-Quest

Editor

Kappa Delta Pi Publications

I

SCIENTIFIC METHOD AND THE CITIZEN

Every generation of leaders has its own Promethean enterprise. The one I would claim for this generation is to bring to men, not fire, for they have too much of that already, but the clear and selfless thinking that Prometheus himself enjoyed. It is to renew once more the oldest, most hopeless, and most glorious of teaching tasks, to help men learn from science, not from passion. It is to do this because, at the present moment, this more than anything else will advance the democracy of civilization.

A man cannot think, however, unless he can also learn. Knowledge and effective thought cannot be made two separate functions of the mind, as if one part of the brain were a basket and the other a blade. A man must have access to knowledge if he would think, and he must also care about the quality of his thinking. He must be proud to think clearly and bravely and be ashamed of brave foolishness. So a democracy of civilization now would mean that more of our citizens would have new freedom in being freely admitted to the treasures of learning, new freedom in learning how to use their minds to solve the problems of human happiness, and feel a new deep loyalty to those endeavors.

This is a difficult time to be asking men to learn to think. So many are urging them not to think, saying that it is neither necessary nor safe, that you would expect to find them very little interested. Their native impulse in that direction is meager at best. Abroad they are told to "think with their blood" which, if not utterly meaningless, is a contradiction in terms. Or, they are told that they have leaders who are "always right" and that these leaders do not need their little help in deciding what to do. Men can scarcely be blamed for listening to these urgings. There is suffering enough. Why add the ache of thinking to the ache of life?

If one wants, still more, to ask men to learn

to think scientifically, dispassionately, freely as against authority and humbly before the facts, he is foolhardy. Let us admit that, at the beginning. This is a Promethean enterprise we are proposing, and you have not forgotten what happened to Prometheus. We have no record of what he thought about, chained to the rock, unless we want to take the poets' word for it. But we can be sure that what he cared for most was the sight of fire burning on the hearths of men, flame he had stolen for them from the gods.

We are members of a pioneering race, and we take our sympathy with Prometheus for granted. But we must not forget that he was more than a popular hero; he was also, for the pious, an example of mistaken zeal. There were many in the myth-growing times of Greece, as there are many around us now, who call it a crime against Heaven to spread those common, observable, and dangerous knowledges like the use of fire. If I am asking you to try again to get men to think scientifically, I realize that it is dangerous to you and to them. Leaders who try it should guard their livers well; the birds of Jupiter are on the wing.

3

The myth of Prometheus is, we may suppose, a poetic trace in history of the life of some hero of the Greek people, some man who got immortality by caring not so much for himself as to help other men. Or it may be the fixation in fable of an ideal that no remembered person ever did embody in actual time. We may suppose that the story was meant to tell us that the gods are jealous of their power. There is no record, we are bound to observe, that the Titan ever got any gratitude for what he did, nor any better reward than perpetual clawing at his liver perpetually renewed, until the gods at last allowed Hercules to free him—as a favor to Hercules.

It may be worthwhile to look closely at this story, partly religious, partly philosophical. It can be matched in somewhat different versions in the folk lore of other peoples, showing that it represents something deep in human thought. We ought to look at it closely because Prometheus was a teacher. He was the first, perhaps, who was ever concerned with what we now call "adult education."

The Titan knew what he was doing when he

4

stole the fire. He carried it in a hollow fennel stalk and gave it to men so they could warm themselves and fry their meat and more efficiently destroy their enemies. This outraged the gods, who are almost never described in the Greek stories as generally benevolent to men. You would think that the slow-moving, myth-making voice of the people says that Prometheus, the thief, got about what he deserved. A curious irony. We accept what our teachers do for us; we seldom thank them.

That, however, is a side issue. I begin with Prometheus because the struggle between men and the gods for the knowledge that is power has been going on almost from the beginning. Democracy of political rights and of social status has been won many times in varying degrees, although never completely. Democracy of civilization, the full sharing, by right of birth, by every man, to the measure of his native powers in all the values of a national culture, that is the last to be gained. Primitive peoples, living in fear and hunger, often share what values they have. And, indeed, their spiritual possessions may be great. We speak now of the dynamic, the modern peoples who find all kinds of justice more difficult.

The fight for knowledge and the fight for democracy are the same battle. Western men have learned to love freedom. You can take it away from them only if first you cut them off from knowledge. The teacher is the creator of freedom because he helps men to know what choices there are in the world and the consequences that follow. And, since the time of the first Prometheus, the fight for knowledge has been going on against all kinds of hindrances, some of which were human.

A democracy of civilization is not, however, limited to a more widespread sharing in the cultural heritage. That is only part of it. A few culturally privileged members of society may have exclusive possession of the most valuable elements in current civilization while the rest of the citizenry have only the treasures of the past, just as it is possible for a small part of society to enjoy a very large share of economic goods or of power, while the others work in their factories or on their land. You cannot say that proletarians do not share in industrialism!

6

The trouble is that they share the burden but not the reward.

In a true cultural democracy, the elements that are typical and the best would be widespread among the people. In our day—at this time—the most valuable possession we have that is not widespread among the people is the scientific attitude of mind.

This is not to say that it is more valuable than other elements which are now well distributed but only that it is so important that we cannot really achieve a cultural unity until we have spread it more widely, until it becomes a characteristic of our whole social living. We speak of a scientific attitude of mind. Knowledge is essential but it is not enough; the method is more important. Prometheus, of course, brought fire, not the lore of how to make it. In sober truth, it was long after men learned the uses of fire that they found out how to kindle it at will. The discoverer of the method, being a scientist, was soon forgotten. What men want now from those who are in power is not only the picture of the world that scientific method makes but enough mastery of the method for themselves to let them use it in their own lives.

No cultural democracy is being achieved if the more powerful groups have kinds of knowledge and methods of thought that are not accessible to all the people. This is the most difficult and a very late phase of democratic progress. Other phases must precede it, and all of history would not be too long a time for the work of preparing its substantiation.

In America we have a large measure of political democracy. We can have more, of course, and we shall have more as we find clear ideas of what it is we want and devise practical plans for their embodiment.

We have been talking, quite recently, a good deal about industrial democracy. It is difficult to know what men mean by the term; they use it in so many different ways. Some speak of industrial democracy as if they mean a general equality of income, for every man to get the same wage. This may be desirable. We are not at the moment required to discuss it. But it was never a basic idea in the democratic thinking of the eighteenth century out of which our system grew. And the only modern country to try it,

Russia, has long since abandoned equal wages as impractical.

Others speak of industrial democracy as if they mean equality of opportunity in the economic struggle. This is undoubtedly a part of the American tradition, of the American dream. To some extent, we have lost it and want it back.

A real industrial democracy would be none of these things. It would be achieved by setting up a different purpose and a different method in industry. It would be managing industry for the sake of workers and not for the sake of the work; for men, not for goods.

Examine this idea in the light of our experience with political self-government. There are, of course, the wordmongers who get themselves into useless arguments on the question of whether the United States is a "democracy" or a "republic." But most of those who speak of the subject now begin with the idea that our faith is in a doctrine for life, for politics, for social organization, having this basic principle: that the individual person is of supreme worth. All social machinery should be devised to give to unique personalities, to living and breathing people, the greatest possible deference and opportunity. This is opposed to the Statism of the Fascists by reason of its concreteness in men and women, whereas Fascists worship an abstraction, the State, of which one man is the glamorous index.

If the individual is the end in a democratic way of life and all things else are means, a political democracy is a political system in which the wisdom of any decision taken is secondary to the educational value, the growth value, of the process of deciding. We govern ourselves, not primarily in order to get a good government, although that seems to be a very good way of getting it, but to grow into better human beings by making up our minds, by acting, and taking the consequences. What we do with our government is instrumental. The end in view is the effect of the experience on ourselves. Educators know that we learn and grow by making decisions for ourselves, not by having them made for us, no matter how wise the imposed decisions might be.

There is, of course, a natural resistance in all men to the trouble of ruling themselves. It is part of the natural desire to avoid effort and to escape responsibility. It is especially strong among the young, at times, when in their un-determined moods they want to be commanded and sacrificed. On that account, we cannot ex-pect any but nations that have come of age to desire or to practice self-government although, naturally, a decaying nation might throw it away. In their prime, men can face the painful stretching of their powers that is demanded by democratic self-government. The principle is clear.

When we turn to a desirable industrial democ-racy, the principle should continue to be clear. It is not for the sake of better industry but for better workers, better men and women, that we want industrial democracy. Here, as in politics, it means self-government. We have it only inso-far as men are responsible for their own eco-nomic destinies, free to make mistakes and to suffer for them. Democracy is the sharing of action and responsibility for the sake of indi-vidual development. This can be done in indus-try only when we consider the living experience of the workers, of all kinds and on all levels, more important than the quantity or quality of the material product turned out. This will take a long time and will require deep changes in our thinking.

May I apply the principle in the same way to this still further stage in democracy that we are talking about, democracy of civilization. Here also there must be, if there is anything real, an equality of responsibility. Equal opportunities mean nothing if equal responsibility does not go with them, because it is the responsibility that is ultimately valuable. This is basic democratic doctrine.

When we have in the future a democracy of civilization, it will be possible because we shall be devoting knowledge to humane purposes. And this is meant in no narrow sense. Man's purposes include watching the swinging of the stars and making music. I mean that humanity as a whole can then, in a democracy of civilization, enjoy all human things.

All human things are not gifts, however, at the hands of others. The most human thing of all is to create. A scientific humanist says, "The main purpose of man is to create such intangible values as beauty, justice, truth." [1] In a true democracy of civilization all men would have the chance, in agreement with their powers, to help make these values that they live by.

Above all, the making, the *poesis* of truth. Men have, in the past, shared much more in a common search for beauty and for goodness than they have in the conquest of nature by rational intelligence. So we say that what they most need now, the greatest virtue they could gain, would be learning how to use the methods by which rational intelligence works—the method of science.

This is a plea more timely than you may think. Surely no one now believes that democracy is being attacked by nations whose armies are looking only for loot. Whatever leaders may want, men are fighting for power and military glory, and behind these is the deep strength of Fascist devotion. It is devotion to an ideal. We think the ideal is false, but that does not change the fact that it is an ideal and that Fascism, and more especially Nazism, holds the hearts of

[1] George Sarton, *History of Science and the New Humanism* (Harvard University Press, 1937).

13

young men by offering something more than material gain.

At least one profound student of the rise of Nazism says that Hitler's appeal to the little people of Germany was that he would give them what they had never had before, a share in the culture of the Fatherland.

Hitler could assemble the hates and resentments of the broken and dispossessed. He could trick the cupidity of the great holders of industrial power with promises. He could offer up the Jews as scapegoats. And he could revive the old illusion of German invincibility. All these things were not enough. He had also to persuade the little people that he had something to give them. He asked for sacrifice, and he offered to make them great because they would be full partners in a greater Reich.

Whatever else you may think of this, it is certain that we must realize once more that it is sentimental to think that men move only for economic reasons. Or that after political democracy and then industrial democracy, they will be finally satisfied. Men will never be finally satisfied, we can be sure. The important point is to prophesy what they will want next. I am saying that they will want more knowledge and more freedom for knowledge because the greatest power that lies in any man's reach today is the power of thought. The aristocrats of today are the men and women who move easily among the treasures of knowledge because they can think with dispassionate power. That is the fire which the jealous gods withhold.

We want to try again and to try harder to get men to learn to think. To prove that the attempt is wise, we can prophesy the good that might come out of even small success. It is probably dangerous for any man to make an inventory of what he thinks might result in the lives of men and women if the present riches of civilization could be open to more of them. Any list is too short, it will suggest limits. I would have you imagine for yourselves what benefits there might be, material and spiritual, in a democracy of civilization.

The sons of Prometheus, however, are not likely to succeed in thieving from the gods unless they know not only what it is they are out to steal and give away, but also what they think the new gift will be worth to men.

I am willing to risk saying what I think will come as a result of taking this next forward democratic step. If men can learn to think more clearly and more dispassionately, they will have more control over their material environment and even over their own selves. We have bent the physical elements to our own purposes with astonishing success in about three hundred years. Our purposes have been childish and destructive sometimes, and too often they have been benevolent but shortsighted. The physical control is still successful, but the human enterprise has made only a slow, precarious gain. When our purposes have been foolish, we could control everything but ourselves, understand everything but each other. It is time to stop using intelligence only for tricks of practice and apply it to the largest aspects of human affairs.

A greater democracy of civilization would mean a more widely shared knowledge of the nature of the physical world and a more sympathetic understanding of the ways and reasons of scientists.

It would mean, while we were understanding better the physical world and managing it therefore more securely, that we would care less about mere physical convenience. We would use our energies to gain less in goods and more in freedom.

There would be a wider spread of economic goods but, in accord with what has just been said, less concern for them, and we might in time learn to value material things because they give us spiritual opportunity.

We would have less provincialism, less intolerance, less narrow and destructive pride.

We might—and this is what I hope for most, holding it as a value that grows out of all these others as a culmination—we might learn to make more general and peaceful judgments. In social, political, and business questions we might learn to care more for the impersonal truth than to have our own "truth" prevail, to fear fanaticism more than defeat, in argument or action. We might thus hope to make civilization kindly and humane. I see no reason for thinking it would be less energetic and I am deeply certain that energy would then be put to better use.

We can go back now and examine these goods more closely. They are well tangled up, each in all the others; we might say they are all phases of an attitude. It is quite evidently an attitude that cannot dogmatically assert its own superiority, since it condemns the fanatic. I would exemplify it by being willing to work with any man who says he seeks quite different ends in making civilization accessible to more people, provided he will in good faith help men to think and learn. If he will help to acquaint people with all kinds of beauty and all kinds of wisdom, if he will enlarge their knowledge of what the world offers and let them choose in the light of that greater knowledge and by more skillful thinking, we can go together. This would be practicing deception on such an ally really, because of my believing all along that if he works for the discovery and the development of all the latent capacities of men he will produce the true, the beautiful, and the good. If they turn out to be different from what I now think, I too shall gain by that surprise.

Men often live in ignorance. That is true, but it is also true that they are naturally hungry to know more than they do. Schools do not create the hunger. They may even dull it into apathy or, what is worse, put ignorant certainties in the place of honest ignorance. But a successful education sharpens and directs in channels of cumulative effect the energy of that native esurience of the mind. It makes it more efficient. Men love this effort as they also love their ease. The pulsations of energy and rest are as natural to the healthy mind as to a healthy body.

We can be quite confident about the natural appetite for precise knowledge. Those who have taken part in the enterprises that we call adult education are often discouraged, of course, but seldom by the thought that people do not want to learn, above all to learn "the truth." What they mean by that dangerous word is usually the measurable and tangible kinds of conclusions about the material world that we call natural science.

For them to be fed this very healthy pabulum, however, is not by any means enough. For their ultimate satisfaction and for social reasons, they will need to go further, not only to listen when the scientist describes in "laws" the features of their world, but also to watch him and understand him while he is at work. And they must learn to let him work in his own way.

They must even learn that his work is not done only with gadgets, with gigantic atom smashers or telescopes. He has also a brain full of webbed abstractions and he is as much the scientist in thinking as he is in the spectacular act.

For the sake of science itself, as good politics for science, more people should understand what science tries to do and what the worker with scientific training calls success. To understand science does not mean to know what button to push to get the expected response from a gadget any more than salesmanship is psychology. It is highly important, of course, that we know what push buttons will bring what mechanical results. This machine world is a dangerous one, and electricity must be "understood" by a modern child as a sailor understands the sea. But the worker who is storing up precise knowledge of phenomena needs our intelligent support, and this requires that we shall not try ignorantly to direct his operations. What I am saying amounts to this: that if science is to be of most use to humanity in general, humanity in general must not undertake to tell scientific workers how they are to do their work. Paradoxical, perhaps, but true. And the two reasons for this have already been given. The scientist must be understood so that he can be helped. That is the reason on behalf of society. His methods must be sympathetically understood because they are in themselves enlightening and strengthening to the mind. That is the reason on behalf of the student. We are here most concerned with this second, this educational value of a knowledge of the scientific method.

It is my own belief—something for which it is impossible to offer experimental proof but still a firm conviction—that the other social goods that I have listed will come as a natural development and elaboration of this first achievement. If we can so diffuse knowledge, so educate the world on all age levels that the method may be really understood, the thinking of the average, intelligent man will have in greater degree than now the several characteristics of this method. These are (and others, of course, might be added) an honest effort to keep his emotions and his desires from fooling him in his thinking, a willingness to keep moral judgments from obscuring his practical judgments, no loss of self-respect because of a suspended opinion, a scrupulous conscience as to the means he uses for any purpose, and implied in all this a sportsmanlike willingness to accept the result. Sportsmanship is a basic virtue in the world that a democracy of civilization would create. Without it culture is meager and democracy is impossible.

In the long run, I suppose, we should have no use for our reason if we did not have emotions. In a very real sense, reason should be the servant of emotion; but reason cannot serve emotion unless it is free. That is to say, we cannot shape the world to our own values unless we search objectively for facts and adjust our purposes to the realities, and unless we work in a world where other men also may search for the truth as they see it.

This enterprise is the more foolhardy, of

course, for one who does not feel certain that scientific thinking can finally determine the ends that men can best pursue. The unemotional rigors of science are, I believe, instruments for the use of ideal purposes. But they are also corrective of those ideals and—what is of most importance—there are certain destructive and vicious ideals widely believed in today that are incompatible with scientific thinking. There are kinds of statesmen who can work only by spitting out blackness like a squid, and men have to struggle to see clearly in their neighborhood. One of their techniques is to destroy science if they can. Science may not teach us what is of most worth; but it is hated by men who are crazy for power because it shows up the speciousness of so much that passes for good. I believe, however, and I am asking you to believe, that the quality men most lack now and most need now is this questioning clarity of thought. They have emotions and drives and ideals—yes, even ideals aplenty. What they need is more exact knowledge of the world and of themselves.

This scientific thinking, this skepticism and

self-criticism you are talking about, I can hear many saying, is just what we have been trying, and it brought us to our present trouble. We followed cold reason, and it brought us cold comfort. We can believe that the same thing probably happened to Prometheus also. Imagine a scene. The Titan has an idea; he is planning something, and he confides in a friend. Why not steal fire from the gods, in a fennel stalk, say— and let all these men and women and children have the use of it? His friend points out the appalling power of Zeus and his notorious bad temper. One thing is sure. Someone tried to dissuade him. So now, they try to dissuade us, saying that this is not a world in which anyone can afford to think. There are too many madmen abroad, and a judicious infection of madness for ourselves is the only thing that will save us. The answer to both these objections is, of course, that we never did really get men to thinking clearly. We never succeeded in that effort if we ever honestly made it and so it cannot be blamed for any present difficulty. Since we have never tried thought as a weapon against madmen, we cannot say that it does not work. The

24

only thing we do know as a result of experience is that violence, even if inevitable in human affairs, is never decisive except to destroy. More of that at the proper time.

II

THE NATURE OF SCIENTIFIC
METHOD

We can persist then in urging upon the leaders
and teachers of our time that their task is still
to teach reason and that the special form of
reason now most needed, and indeed most difficult to achieve, is what we call scientific thinking. The words, however, are used in many
ways. It is scientific to give precise and arbitrary
meaning to one's terms, and we can pause to
follow that rule. What do we mean by "scientific" and what by "science"?

It is all too customary to call this a scientific
age. We are surrounded by gadgets, push buttons, and magic currents, and we blame the
laboratory workers, by whom we are also surrounded, for this mechanical bliss. We are, when
more thoughtful, aware that most of us are

alive because knowledge has thwarted the disease that otherwise would have killed us as it killed our fathers. We are aware of a kind of warmth in life, not too comfortable, that is the result of our numerousness and the extent to which we live in each other's presence because of communication and transportation and too many contacts. The world is more than cosy; it is congested. We live *by* science in large measure, but that, unfortunately, does not tell us what science is nor assure us that we really care anything about it.

One sign that the age is not really deserving of the adjective "scientific" is that men in white coats and spectacles, and very often with beards, and coming usually from some place like Vienna, are "authority" for almost anything. "Science" offers us cosmetics that penetrate the skin and secrets that defeat congenital stupor. It is a first principle in scientific thinking that one is skeptical of all authority. We are, in this age, generally so lacking in scientific manners that we make science itself authoritarian.

By science, I mean all the accumulated descriptions of the world that can be made without adjectives of value. They make no claim to absoluteness or permanence, these descriptions, but they serve for operational forecasts. They can be submitted to all the tests of common sense and they are public matters, not the private experience or revelation of any chosen few. And by scientific method, we mean the habit of seeking such facts and of accepting them, if they appeal to the logic of our sensory tests, no matter what they may do to previous generalities.

The scientist is in one sense the thinker who cares more for means than for ends. As Cohen and Nagel have put it: [1]

Science does not desire to obtain conviction for its propositions in *any* manner and at *any* price. Propositions must be supported by logically acceptable evidence, which must be weighed carefully and tested by the well-known canons of necessary and probable inference. It follows that the *method* of science is more stable, and more important to men of science, than any particular result achieved by its means.

In virtue of its method, the enterprise of science is a self-corrective process. It appeals to no special

[1] Morris R. Cohen and Ernest Nagel, *An Introduction to Logic and the Scientific Method* (Harcourt Brace, 1934), p. 395.

revelation or authority whose deliverances are indubitable and final. It claims no infallibility, but relies upon the methods of developing and testing hypotheses for assured conclusions. The canons of inquiry are themselves discovered in the process of reflection, and may themselves become modified in the course of study. The method makes possible the noting and correction of errors by continued application of itself.

Or, to put it more shortly, now that we know what we are talking about and we need not hedge our terms so carefully, science is knowledge that can be tested in experience and communicated to others. [2]

Science exists, in Hogben's terms, "in the public world." In that world we are responsible to others for what we believe and for what we refuse to believe. Our ideas are not our private affair, and we cannot shield them from an attack, no matter how destructive, if it comes also in the public world and by way of rational proof.

For this kind of thought, we claim no infallibility, as Cohen says, because it is essential to

[2] Cf. Wilbur Marshall Urban, *Language and Reality* (Macmillan, 1939), p. 745.

the point of view here described that the one who proposes an idea should be himself the most anxious to give it a stern test. For example, I know a young biologist who is being trained in this strict tradition. Not long ago he had an idea, a creative hunch, that promised to throw some light on a very difficult problem. When asked if he had told the head of the laboratory, his chief, about it, he protested, "Oh, no! It will take me several months to find out first if I can't prove that I'm wrong." This struck me as different from the attitude of some of my colleagues, who rush all new notions into print as quickly as possible for fear they may be proved wrong by someone else. They are more anxious to bear intellectual offspring than to have them legitimate. Of course, there are flaws in the education of young scientists, serious ones as we may later discover, but this virtue is real. And is it necessary to point out that when men think in this fashion they do not burn heretics?

We are not talking about everything that calls itself by the fashionable name. Our subject is the form of knowledge that disclaims authority and asks you to test conclusions for yourself, that makes no boast of getting at any ultimate "reality" at all. In the theories of its purest types it disclaims even the power of "explanation." Into these refinements of philosophy of science it is not necessary for us to go. The chief thing to be noted now is a moral quality. The kind of thinking we are talking about is essentially modest. It claims as little as possible and will accept any man's question.

This kind of scientific thinking is not, however, "pure" in the sense of being never applied. A good deal of confusion has been brought into the discussion of the so-called "social" sciences recently by accusations that some men are collecting facts and drawing principles therefrom without caring what was done with their ideas and not even caring whether the problems they try to solve are or are not important. "Important" is not a word that means anything by itself. Important to whom? For what? The debate appears to be nothing more than a way of expressing the natural discomfort that comes from failure to make sure in the beginning that you know what you are talking about.

Social sciences, like all others, have their research and their engineering aspects. Both aspects are scientific in the real sense, and there is a good deal of fruitful interchange between them. But their functions are cleanly distinguished. A research worker judges a problem by its theoretical importance; an engineer by its practical importance. Their collaboration rests on that understanding. For our purposes it is important only to note that they are both committed to the same intellectual virtues, and that these virtues are not lessened if knowledge is put to practical use.

Of these applications we all know a good deal, perhaps too much, because we clutter our lives with devices besides taking advantage of more important things made possible for us. What else do we do to make good the claim of our age to being "scientific"? To some extent, we support the necessary men and institutions. What we fail to do is to learn the method. We admire but we do not imitate. Outside their special preoccupations, and their special kind of saintliness, scientific workers are no more worthy of imitation and no less than other men. I have already said that there is no special health in giving them deference. If, however, they are men who care more for method than for results, we can say that we care more for their method than for themselves. The impersonality of the whole transaction should be preserved. In every consideration the crucial element is the method.

It may well be asked why we urge that all men should learn to lead better lives by applying impersonal thinking to their pursuit of happiness when we must admit that scientists themselves are seldom better than the rest of us. There are two answers to this skeptical question. One is that scientists are often much better than the rest of us in one important quality; they are seldom fanatics. The other answer is that they fall short of virtue—when they do— almost entirely because of failure to be scientists at all when they are outside the laboratory. When they are able to study their own affairs with even a little of the detachment they give to the natural world, they show clearly enough the virtues we are seeking.

Anyone who proposes to teach a difficult method of thinking to all men should doubtless pause to consider how capable of thinking men are and what differences in ability are found among them. Do our present measures of intelligence tell us all we need to know?

There is a battle on over the alleged stability of the IQ. Like most such battles it is fought among apostles rather than among the inventors of important faiths. In the writings of the psychologists who first set up the IQ measures of intelligence you will find only reasonable claims for their stability and exactness. But the IQ was a handy tool for quick classification of human beings. Busy school officials like handy tools and tend to overvalue them.

Outside the school, also, there was a natural approval of the doctrine that children had fixed, unchanging native capacities. The doctrine was used to prop those social tendencies that would keep men in fixed classes, a tendency we call "fascistic," although that is only a new name for a natural and ever recurring desire. A generation or two ago we had what was called "social Darwinism" and we put men into fixed groups by what we called their "fitness to survive." Now we have in some quarters something we might call "social IQ-ism," the doctrine of determining what a human being can do even before he has had any chance to do it.

So there have been reasons, quite scientific ones, for pronouncing judgments somewhat too final on individual differences in capacity. The genes of men do mix in infinitely various ways. People, living human beings, are marvelously different from one another, and in all possible characters some are better and some worse. Men differ, we say, and it may be that they differ greatly in the capacity to acquire the habit of rigorous thought. It may be that only a few in any generation can ever learn to perceive and accept the evidence of their senses and follow their own reasoning to its end. But it may also be possible that our social environment and our schools do not encourage or develop these qualities in most of our people and that their structural capacities are unknown.

Differences in "general" intelligence do not necessarily determine special capacities. We are here discussing the ability to learn a method, a special use of intelligence for which there are doubtless degrees of aptitude, but which might possibly be developed to some degree in everybody. It would seem likely, of course, that those who have brains of higher general power will have this ability as part of their equipment. But that does not always happen, and single traits are oddly assorted. There have been men with surpassing artistic gifts whose ability to think in objective terms was quite childish. I would call Tolstoy a good illustration. On the other hand, persons of scientific capacity who are intelligent in the general way are sometimes insensitive to art. Or, they may seem more incapable than they are because they talk too much about subjects they have not studied. The point of importance for the educator is that the capacity for learning to think straight may be present in some degree in nearly all human beings. There is no conclusive reason for deciding that it is a special gift.

We are told insistently by some students of children that scientific thought is naturally alien to the temperament of some human beings. The contrast is usually made, not between science and stupidity, but between science and poetry. There are those who delight in the imagination, we are told, and who are, on that account, not interested in the crass materialism of scientific thought. We have already pointed out that the method here described can be used, and commonly is used, to deal with all kinds of material and that science need not be grubby. At the same time, it may be necessary to repeat that the imagination is present in all thought. Imagination is not busy only with dreams.

The nub of a fancied opposition between a material, precise, and pedestrian discipline in science and the free burgeoning of the spirit in the arts lies elsewhere. For the arts are not free, as many people romantically believe. There is no discipline that man puts upon himself more stiff and arduous than the discipline that goes into the making, or indeed into the intelligent appreciation, of music or painting or literature. Just as science requires the same bold and vigorous imagination that is needed in the arts, so the arts require as noble and self-sacrificing discipline as does science. When Goethe said *"Alles muss bezahlt werden,"* he was speaking of all the values that there are in life. Human values are all earned.

The distinction between getting the habit of

careful and objective thinking in all one's affairs and getting mastery in some field of art is real enough. Some men have been able to work on the highest levels of both kinds of thinking; most of us enjoy both on some level in our daily experience. When we consider not the specially gifted personalities but the children in our schools, most judgments of the possibilities are superficial and hasty. We are often told, for example, that some child is good in language but just cannot get mathematics. The child himself will offer this description of his abilities, although he is usually honest enough to describe his likes and dislikes rather than his good and bad equipment. Not all scientific thought is mathematical, of course, but mathematics is a language for the expression of abstract relations, and those who find difficulty in thinking abstractly in this language of non-verbal symbols are very likely to find abstract thinking of any kind either distasteful or unbearably difficult. So we divide the children into sheep and goats, and they connive in this distinction. Some of them are, as we say, "literary," and others are "good in mathematics," which later becomes "good in science."

A good many students of teaching methods have pointed out that the teaching of mathematics may be so badly done that the child is needlessly repelled. No doubt this is true. It happens also, it seems, in teaching literature or the arts. But I do not believe that we can, without further examination of the data, jump to the conclusion that children are really artistic sheep and scientific goats. It is not so simple as that.

We must first take into account the fact that to think abstractly is a somewhat later event in the maturation of a normal mind than to think in colorful images. This suggests that mathematics is offered to some children before they have grown up to do it. More important is the fact that abstract and objective thinking is actually a more artificial way of thinking than the image-making that will suffice, for example, in the simple stages of learning to read a poem. Without stretching the genetic parallel too far, we can still take into account the probability that man made myths long before he could count the toes on his second foot. Whether he ought to have stayed in the myth-making stage and never have learned to count is a question we have begged in the beginning. We are talking about a new Prometheanism that looks forward, not back, to a golden age.

If abstract and objective thinking is more difficult, more artificial, and comes later in the child's development, we should look carefully into our ways of teaching. We might see brutality in our presentation of mathematics. In his first lessons in reading the child is called upon to exercise his image-making powers. He is also encouraged at the same stage to react emotionally to sounds in music, to symbols and representation in pictures, to words in literature. And this is quite as it should be. The child first learns to react to symbols with recognition and vivid feeling.

Then, brutally, he is presented with the abstract symbols of mathematics, and the one reaction that he is not allowed to make is the emotional one. Mathematicians in their maturity talk of the beauty of pure forms and the elegance of symbolic manipulations. These are genuine aesthetic values, no doubt, but they are not for babes. No, the child generally does not even have it explained to him that he is now entering a world in which his learned reactions to other symbols are no longer welcome. He must now begin to repress his emotions and follow logical relations with artificial care.

This process does separate children into those who can and those who cannot "get" mathematics. But it has no necessary relation to their individual differences in native capacity. It sorts out, not the bright child from the dull, nor the poetic from the material, nor the scientific from the literary, but only the lucky from the unfortunate.

We cannot, at this point, go into the pedagogy of teaching children how to think abstractly and impersonally. But I must acknowledge in passing that the process is here much over-simplified. I do not mean to say that there is no emotion, or should be no emotion in learning mathematics. The emotion involved, however, should clearly be attached to the sense of achievement and the desire to think effectively. It should not

41

be the summoning up of emotion-carrying images that is the natural reaction to art.

It would seem only prudent and intelligent on our own part to make an honest trial of teaching all children to think straight before we blame failure to do so on native incapacity. If we do our best to teach them and then see that we have failed, there is still something else to do before we give up.

We know that there is at least a fringe of native capacity in the school population, a fringe of boys and girls who can learn to think. They respond with industry and understanding to the chance to sharpen their perceptions and learn clear logic. These, at least, we should train because they will inherit civilization. In the time of the next generation, civilization will be in their keeping.

Those left over, those who cannot learn to think in this special fashion we are talking about, would be, I suppose, of two kinds. At least, those who insist on their existence make two groups of them. The first group is made up of those who are sensitive, imaginative, and so subjective that they must always think with passion and at their peril. Some writers appear to believe that the artists of the future will probably be found in this group. I may be permitted to doubt it. What I am sure of is that there will be found in this group the human beings doomed to make a general mess of life.

It should be remembered that I do not believe any child really belongs in such a group of gifted children who cannot learn to think. Little Tolstoys are not running around in all our classrooms. For one child who is really so responsive to the stimuli of his senses and so vibrant in his nerves that he must feel only and respond only with feeling, I believe that there are hundreds who are led into a mush-fibered helplessness by bad teaching. And contrariwise, I do not believe there are many children who are naturally deaf to music, blind to pictures, and dull to the drama of great literature. Being able to think never made them so. Bad homes, bad health, bad teaching—other things may have spoiled for them the great experiences of their own emotions, but not too much logic.

However, if we can believe the pessimists, there is still another group which comprises a lot of low-grade minds into whose dimness no light can ever go. These children, we are told, are incapable of ever thinking in clear logical patterns, incapable of grasping abstractions or scientific laws or the rigors of scientific method. What are we to do with them?

If they have not minds, they do at least have emotions. Insofar as these incapables exist, and to the extent that they are proved to exist, we cannot dodge a direct responsibility to train them emotionally to be attached and loyal to the institutions which more clear-thinking children create and maintain. This is a large and tough problem. All I can say here is that if there are children incapable of acquiring their equal share of culture, they must be taught to be loyal to those who can. Civilization itself cannot be cut down to their size. We are still far from trying nearly hard enough to teach them all they can learn. When we have an environment for every child and for every mature person, all through life, which is good enough to give all his latent powers a chance to grow, and if then we find some of them incorrigibly stupid in solving their own problems, unworthy to help in solving the

44

problems of all of us, we can relax the effort to bring them up to par. We are still a long way from any such place or certainty. In the meantime, we must teach all of them the loyalties that make the thoughtless fit companions for those who have learned to think.

There is another objection to the idea of teaching all men to use the methods of objective thinking in their serious affairs that is based not on men's limited capacity but on the weight and difficulty of all technical masteries. No one can be an expert, it is said, in everything. In fact, only a few devoted persons can be really expert in anything. The rest of us must depend on those who know more than we do for a great many of our most serious decisions. This is quite true. But the role of the expert in democratic living is not to be defined in the same terms as serve to identify a dictator. The expert knows more than we do about technical matters, but that does not give him control over our lives.

We still must decide what questions are to be referred to technically trained servants of the people and what can only be decided by the responsible thinking of those concerned. The best way to make such choices, which become weightier and more crucial as our civilization develops, is to know how the experts think, to sympathize with their habits and to use, when we call them in, the same clear objective thought that we expect them to use in carrying out our orders. And for what we still must decide ourselves, we need to imitate the trained mind as well as we can.

A second comment on this difficulty could be made historically. The great triumphs of technical knowledge have often been achieved by the cooperation of laymen, and often they could not have been achieved in any other way. A good example is the swift reduction of the death rate and the prolongation of average life. This has three phases, and we must not overlook the third. First comes the investigation in laboratories and clinics, whereby the necessary theoretic knowledge of diseases and resistances is built up. Then comes the engineering phase, when sanitary technicians remake the environment. Third is the cooperation of men and women and children who learn to follow the rules and actually permit themselves—by understanding what is expected of them—to be saved.

Scientific method and scientific knowledge are not the same thing. But it appears to be neither desirable nor, indeed, possible to teach one without the other. A public opinion miraculously gifted with scientific caution and a love of accuracy would not be an uninformed public opinion. A student who learns to think straight is soon going to find that his straight thinking gets him knowledge he could not otherwise have. A leader of the people who, instead of egging us on to employ our talent for confusion, began to ask us to use our minds as rigorously as possible on public affairs would soon find it difficult to do anything else because we would know too much. The spread of knowledge and the spread of better mental habits are likely to go together.

We are not content, however, to work only for the spread of knowledge. We are working also for the spread of those habits by which dependable knowledge can be acquired. Ahead of us are both difficulties and encouragements. First, we have the encouraging fact, already mentioned, that men have a love of facts. Even sometimes when they do not know what to do

47

with them; when they cannot fit them together nor add them up to any good purpose, they still love facts. Close observation of those who live on the very lowest levels of our cultural life confirms this, and the amusement of sophisticates over radio quizzes confirms it on another level. But, unfortunately, it is easier to teach most men that a star is a hundred million miles from earth than to get them interested in the manner of finding out that scientific item, and so the love of facts is not enough.

III

THE TEACHING OF SCIENTIFIC
METHOD

Obstacles are thick ahead. There is a complacency in our leaders, obstinacy in the learned, the opposition of pseudo-scientists and of modern authoritarians. Most of these are the old villains in the drama of civilization, difficulties which have always stood in the way of teachers. They are in a true sense the modern replicas of the jealous gods who would deny knowledge to the sons of men. Naturally, the persons who embody these difficulties are often quite unaware of their own rôle. They may even be benevolent. But men can do much evil in the world without ever thinking of themselves as anything but good.

Something like adult education has always existed in great societies and at great periods in history. But an unfeeling ridicule of mature people who wanted to learn and of those who would undertake to teach them has existed also.

The record begins to take on its modern shape about a century ago. Lord Brougham, in England, would have applied the term adult education only to the narrow but necessary job of teaching factory hands to read. But he was very busy with enterprises perhaps more important even than that. He wanted the skill to read made the common possession of all citizens; he also wanted material prepared that they could understand. As a politician and a lawyer Brougham is so nearly forgotten that we often fail to remember his importance in the history of education. He helped to make acceptable the idea, full of blasphemy a hundred years ago, that higher education could be carried on in England by a university not manned and dominated by the church. More important for us, he launched the Society for the Diffusion of Useful Knowledge, which began to publish books in 1827.

The novelists of the day thought he was funny. Peacock has some ill-humored and snob-

bish satire at his expense, and Disraeli in Endym-
ion relates a scrap of talk between a farmer
and a gentleman, written half a century later,
but typical of the time in which it was thought
to be a great joke that a farmer could better
cultivate his fields if he knew something of
chemistry.

Matthew Praed wrote:

But let them not babble of Greek to the rabble,
And teach the mechanics their letters;
The labouring classes were born to be asses,
And not to be aping their betters.

What is not generally realized by some of you
who smile at that silly piece is that whereas
such snobbishness was mostly social then it is
educational or pseudo-intellectual now. The
snobbishness is with us just the same. The trouble with this sort of thing is that it is so often
the unamiable weakness of great men. Thomas
Carlyle, for example, who had personal reasons
for disliking Brougham, objected to the Society
for the Diffusion of Knowledge because "good
books already existed in abundance."

The University of London is now one of the world's great institutions, and I suppose no one would think of it as an outlaw among universities. The Mechanics' Institutions which Brougham helped Birkbeck and the others to establish have mostly passed into inaction. But they are gone only because public libraries and public lectures have been established on a broader basis.

Brougham's other enterprise, the most important of all, publishing cheap books that everybody could read, was never fully a success. Similar popular book schemes have been set up many times since. None has been very successful. We still struggle with the central difficulty. There is still not much serious literature for the great bulk of the population in Brougham's country, or in ours.

One would think that the immense spread of common school education in this country in the last hundred years would have given everybody the needed reading skill to get for himself all the important knowledge that he needs. We are dealing with two variables here. We need to keep them distinct. One is the reading skill of the adult population. The other is the readability of books. They are two reasons for saying that the treasures of knowledge in our culture are not accessible to most of our people. To blame men and women for not making greater use of accumulated treasures of science and art, history and philosophy, is unjust. They cannot use it. They cannot read well enough to acquire it from the books now available. What their real capacity may be is unknown because it has never been given a chance to develop to its natural limits.

A third difficulty that may be of equal importance is that what books there are are not where they can be got at, even if most men and women could read them. One may expect some polite skepticism regarding these points. Some of this skepticism comes from the business and professional men who know all the answers in education. They have never had to solve any of the problems of education and they have as a result the innocent illusions of their youth. Skepticism, disbelief, or hush-hush caution comes also from teachers and librarians. Nobody enjoys facing the truth about the book-reading habits of our population. Nobody likes to admit what every competent person knows.

The civilization that we have is not democratically enjoyed for these reasons that I have been recounting. As for knowledge, an acquaintance with the best that is being thought and done in the world, the average American gets very little. Most people cannot read well enough to understand the books that exist. The books are not accessible to them, even if they could read them. No one is doing more than a small part of what needs to be done to provide them with books that can be understood.

What of the public libraries? We are proud of them and still more proud, I hope, of the devoted and skillful work done by the librarians who operate them for the public good. But in the last year for which figures can be compiled, the year 1937–38, our public libraries spent less than ten cents per person for new reading matter. Not as much as two copies for each person of a five-cent weekly. Even including the meager salaries on which librarians are asked to be public benefactors, their total expenditures were forty-two cents per person. The District of

Columbia spent $1.30 for each person in the district, for all public library purposes. But no state spent as much as one dollar, and nine states spent ten cents or less!

Do people buy books for themselves? The record is the only answer worth considering. In the last recorded year we manufactured, all told, of all kinds, not enough books to give every person two of them. If our people wanted books, where would they get them?

Our complacency is caused, no doubt, by the fact that the only persons who ever think about reading are those who do a great deal, perhaps too much of it, and never think of the millions who live in a bookless world. Teachers and librarians and sociologists inhabit generally a world in which books are almost as important as people, are in fact the embodiment of character and reality, and are much more dependable sources of useful knowledge than one's friends. Their complacency may be understod. That does not excuse it. The chance to enjoy what the great men and women of today and yesterday have created for us fixes on us the duty to do what we can to give to others that same chance.

There is also public education, the foundation structure. If compared with other professional workers, educators are not a complacent lot. Most gatherings of professional workers in other fields give forth sounds that strike the ear of the outsider as the cooings of mutual approval or gang solidarity. The sounds that rise from conferences of teachers are more warlike. Teachers are always reforming education or each other and occasionally get around to reforming themselves.

This honesty has made educational thinking, not perfect, but essentially fluid although our school systems, and our actual schools and colleges find it quite impossible to keep up with the changes that theorists and philosophers propound. However, this admirable preoccupation with what education ought to be often blinds teachers to the facts of what American education actually is. We cannot fairly call this complacency, but it has much the same practical results.

In the first place, education for the young is still meager and uneven in our country. We cannot expect children to learn to think on an adult level if they get nothing but a brief and bad school experience.

Parents and statesmen may be forgiven for ignorance about the true success of our century-old attempt, begun by Horace Mann, to educate everybody reasonably well. Teachers ought to know. Let me hasten to say that this is not another one of those easy attacks upon the quality and direction of American public education which can be worked up by any pseudo-professor and applauded by all the people whose education he condemns. The quality of American public school education is immensely varied, but it is, if at all measurable as a whole, a great success. The trouble with most of our American citizens is not that American education is bad but that they never got any.

College freshmen may not be what their instructors want them to be. That is a difficulty that counts both ways. But when a philosopher looks upon the conduct of the American public and finds it wanting in wisdom or patience and says, "You see what the American high school—

and the American college—does to people?
Ruins 'em!" he is talking solemn and cruel non-
sense.

The present American adult population is
only in a very small part the product of the
American public school system. Of the 80,-
000,000 voting adults in this country, less than
3,000,000 ever went to any college. Less than
11,000,000 ever went through any kind of high
school. This is one in seven to go through a high
school, and of these not many in middle life
went through the kind of high school we would
consider good enough today. They were, and
still are, the products of the high schools of
twenty, thirty, forty years ago.

We are doing as well now as we ever did in
secondary education, better probably than any
other nation ever did. But we have only about
two-thirds of the eligible children actually in
school in the secondary grades even now. And,
contrary to a popular folk belief, there is nothing
retroactive about education. Parents get only
small benefit out of what their children learn.
We have about a seventh-grade average population. This is not a scientific nor an accurate

statistical figure, but it is a fair estimate. The United States Commissioner of Education makes estimates consonant with these, and Dr. Studebaker is not an unfriendly critic of American schools. In fact, these figures are a defense. Our achievements are great; our needs for the future, however, are still greater.

Complacency over the present state of our educational levels, our circulation of books, and our reading habits is a first obstacle because those who are complacent about what has been done stand in the way of doing more. Some of the opposition to a democracy of civilization, however, and especially such a democratic renascence as might come from giving everyone a grasp of scientific ways of thought is more than the passive resistance of those who are complacent or inert. Some of it comes actively from the "medicine men." The medicine men are those in high places in the intellectual world who would keep their knowledge and their skill to themselves.

We are not here much concerned with history. We can remind the medicine men of today that they are following an age-old pattern because that reminder will help them to understand themselves, perhaps, and in any case, it will help us to deal with them. The medicine men, the shamans and the false high priests, have seldom been teachers. Against them the teachers have had to work. The medicine men have been rather like Zeus in this one meanness; they have wanted to keep the fire for themselves.

No one has ever given us a complete picture of the intellectual history of prehistoric times. There have been phases, of course, among all peoples, perhaps long millenniums of time, in which all that was known was held in common by the tribe. But when special knowledge of stars or signs, of weather or some other magic, got built up in the memory of a priest or two, the priest and medicine men knew too well that knowledge was power. They kept it to themselves and made slaves of those who could not learn it. We cannot separate completely the political kind from power of other kinds. Any group of men who know a great deal more than their fellows will be masters. Prometheus, the real teacher, is always in some measure in rebellion against his rulers.

And Zeus chained Prometheus to the rock.

Luckily, the modern inhabitants of Olympus are not quite so insolent and certainly not so powerful.

In one sense there probably should be an aristocracy of the mind. Surely all honor, all protection, all opportunity ought to be accorded to those who have special gifts for learning and for thought. But all aristocracies have their faults, and I am willing to assume full responsibility for saying that in the modern aristocracy of the mind there is little sense of helping those less gifted, or perhaps less fortunate, to understand the world as the learned understand it. There is a real sense of *noblesse oblige*, a sense of deep obligation to the truth and to the values of civilization itself. But there is almost no sense of obligation to the flickering in other men of the same light that makes them great.

The names of scientists and philosophers will rush to your minds to contradict this accusation. There is a blessed company of men who fit that description by Matthew Arnold:

This is the *social idea;* and the men of culture are the true apostles of equality. The great men of culture are those who have had a passion for diffusing, for making prevail, for carrying from one end of society to the other, the best knowledge, the best ideas of their time; who have laboured to divest knowledge of all that was harsh, uncouth, difficult, abstract, professional, exclusive; to humanize it, to make it efficient outside the clique of the cultivated and learned, yet still remaining the *best* knowledge and thought of the time, and a true source, therefore, of sweetness and light. Such a man was Abelard in the Middle Ages, in spite of all of his imperfections; and thence the boundless emotion and enthusiasm which Abelard excited. Such were Lessing and Herder in Germany, at the end of the last century; and their services to Germany were in this way inestimably precious. Generations will pass, and literary monuments will accumulate, and works far more perfect than the works of Lessing and Herder will be produced in Germany; and yet the names of these two men will fill a German with a reverence and enthusiasm such as the names of the most gifted masters will hardly awaken. And why? Because they *humanized* knowledge; because they broadened the basis of life and intelligence; because they worked powerfully to diffuse sweetness and light, to make reason and the will of God prevail.

The truth remains: Young scientists do not learn in our laboratories and schools that science has any responsibility for the education of laymen. Few scientists will take any interest even in the college student if he does not want to attempt a professional scientific career. Scholars in our graduate schools have a special sneer for what is "popular." Learning is a cult. You belong or you do not belong. Let me illustrate. A young physicist told me once in a pleasant clubroom conversation about an idea he had for an article on a matter of wide general interest. Why didn't he write it and try for a good magazine? He was struck with horror. To have his name in *Harper's* or the *Atlantic?* What would his colleagues say? And if you think that young man was misinterpreting the probable attitude of his friends, let me quote from a man of very great scientific distinction who did once write a philosophical article for one of those periodicals. When asked what his laboratory associates thought of his intellectual slumming he smiled guiltily and said, "Oh, it was all right. They just never found out about it."

These incidents are amusing. You may believe that they are not typical enough to mean anything. Most scientists will give lip service to a quite different attitude. But too many of them are still medicine men in a cave, and they do not want the other lay members of the tribe peering in. They cannot refuse to forgive Einstein if he takes the trouble to collaborate with Infeld in a book for amateurs on the theories of physics. But they are not too indulgent toward Eddington and Jeans. And they remonstrate privately with the Shapleys, the Mathers, the Kelloggs, the men who take time and trouble to help enterprises of popularization.

We should be quite clear on one point. No one, I believe, has a right to tell a scientist or a scholar or a philosopher that he must spend his time in this or that or any other way. We can believe in freedom even for great minds! If a man chooses by temperament and the accidents of opportunity to bury himself in library or laboratory and there pursue the lonely and arduous adventures out of which will come new ideas or new knowledge, that is his right. He must be protected in it. We are advocating freedom for the scientist to do his own work in his own way. But we are protesting that this work of making science known to men has got to be done. If scientists will not do it, someone else will do it for them.

IV

THE PLACE OF SCIENTIFIC METHOD IN OUR TIME

There are other hindrances besides the medicine men. We are in a crisis. To some, no doubt, the plea here made will be thought much needed in a critical moment. To others, it will seem out of order—or too late. It is natural for men to turn, in times of great danger, away from thinking, which they learned painfully, back to breathing deep and feeling their muscles, which apes can do as well. Let's stop talking and *do* something! It's an old cry. It is much easier to do the wrong thing than to think a way through to the right one. This is so evident, as we study the nature of man more closely, that there is even a school of thought that comes near to saying that the age-long struggle to make man rational should be given up. Let's just call action thinking, say its believers, and try to make the strength of impulse a proof of good consequences.

There is a superficial current against us, as well as an old deep tide of anti-rational feeling. It seems a pity to have to admit that the intellectual world, or at least the world of scholarship and education and literature—the world of ideas, in short—is subject to mere fashion. One would like to believe that the winds of doctrine are not cyclones. They seem to be, however, unless perhaps it is only that a good many intellectuals are such loyal children of their age that they must never miss a chance to change their philosophy to suit the roar of the mob.

Tempers have been for some time rising in the world about us. When men are angry or afraid, they not only brook no opposition; they do not even want to learn anything to their own good. If, as the good pragmatists say, men think only when they are in trouble, it is plain that they do not think at all if they are in trouble enough. So educators and intellectuals who never really cared much anyhow for the calm and unexciting life of reason have been hustling back along the line of their burned bridges, trying to get into a band wagon that is going in the other direction. This shift in fashion is unfortunate; it need not discourage us.

One doctrine now fashionable needs some examination. It is that we have to ape madness in a mad world. The phrase I use does not remind you of what is being actually said, of course. But that this soberly describes the belief of many people is evident enough. We have all heard intelligent and anxious men say recently that we must fight force with force (which may be true) and that *therefore* we would be wise to stir up bloodthirstiness in ourselves and in each other, more especially in the hearts of young men allotted to the battle. Not many important public voices have said this yet, but we have nightmare memories of twenty-five years ago. Poets and publicists and even some scientists have already indulged in an intemperate and childish anger that encourages less responsible citizens to believe that their leaders accept the program. We have enemies and they hate us. Their fury makes them more dangerous. Hence we must hate them to be dangerous in defense—so goes the theory.

In the first place, without at once going to the heart of the question, we may wonder how men who reason in this way can also maintain that our cause is the just defense of the high values of civilization. If we are really defending the most precious things in the world, freedom and mercy, is not a convinced indignation enough? Do we need to be angry to be certain that we shall not doubt the war's necessity?

This ironic flaw, however, would not deter those who have decided that fury is now noble because ignoble men are furious. It would only irritate them. There is a deeper and a more decisive point. Those who say that at this time we too must "think with our blood," because Hitler is still unconquered, believe that hate will win battles. We may for the moment admit that this might in some measure be true. But we must insist that wars do not decide the fate of nations except by destroying them. Wars are purely destructive, whether they are lost or won. But we are compelled to fight a war, it is said, because determined aggression can be met in no other way. It is like living with a neurotic. One neurotic person can destroy a family and should be suppressed. This may also be true. But it does not change the fact that victory will not solve any problems except the problem of this war. It will not solve the problem of the next war. It cannot because it does not solve the problem of the possible peace.

If this seems like anything but an obvious proposition, it is because we shout at each other so rashly that we cannot hear the voices of the past. We won a war in 1918. We crushed and dismembered the enemy. A generation later we have what—peace? Is more proof needed that we do not establish peace by winning wars but only by wise action after we have won and the chance comes to reconstruct the shattered earth?

The black tribesmen of northeastern Australia, as reported by Lloyd Warner, have so many kinds of fighting that they have names for the varieties. And the one that is "all out," when they intend to kill, is called a "War to End Wars." Our own practice is less naïve and not less foolish.

Any attempt to teach men to think with scientific detachment, to apply rational principles to judgments on human affairs, meets opposition from more than fashion. It meets in many forms the institutions and the preachments of authority. This is natural and in a way very healthy because the kind of thinking here argued for would reduce authority. And it is rash to expect those who defend authoritarian doctrines always to be weak. Here the advocates of judicious angers and the authoritarians join hands. One subtle line of argument they offer is to say that science and positive thought are well enough in their place but that their place is not very important because they can look at only material things.

Man does not live by bread alone; this important and quite evident truth is often urged as if it were a reason against man's knowing more than he does now about his material world. Man lives, also, of course, by judgments on the beautiful and the good. But if this is a moral world, there seems to be no evident reason why more knowledge will make him care less for either beauty or goodness. Indeed, one is suspicious of those whose philosophical or religious judgments are, in their own opinion, threatened by what the scientist calls "facts." The real quarrel, of course, is about something a little different. When we say that men would lead "better" lives if they knew more, there is little to be said against it. However, when we say that they should pursue the good life by the methods of the scientist, with hypotheses tested by sensory data, or guesses tried out by observation, then there is uneasiness among philosophers and theologians. Some of them ask, "Does this mean then that such methods can establish values?" The relation between judgments of fact and judgments of value is so confused that we might well look at it. Education is, presumably, responsible for training judgment in both fields, and teachers can profitably study the difference.

We may list three important relations that these two kinds of judgments might have, knowing that this is not an exhaustive analysis. First, scientific studies may be made of value judgments exactly as studies are made of any other social phenomena, by examining behavior and symbolic uses, or by introspection. No one questions this relation. This is only to say that science can consider value judgments as observed data of experience and try to describe them.

Second, scientific thinking is incompatible, as we have said before, with certain kinds of value judgments. All judgments of both kinds are made in expectation that something will happen. This is not meant as a kind of bastard pragmatism; I mean only that every judgment is based on a belief that the world will go on behaving about as it has in the past, that certain uniformities in the universe will persist. I do not even say that these uniformities are in any sense "true." But they are believed to be true. And when the consequences of a value judgment are brought in question by scientific examination, there are possible cases in which the value judgment will be relinquished because of scientific judgments on experience. This would appear to mean that scientific methods can sometimes correct, or negatively determine, ultimate goods.

A third conceivable relationship between science and value judgments, or, if you like, between science on the one hand and philosophy and religion on the other, is that the hypothesis and sensory-test method will actually discover and define those ultimate goods. This would be the same as saying that science is on the way toward replacing altogether the judgments of theology and religion and that these are only imperfect steps in human progress soon to be surpassed. I am not prepared to say that this is true. It is an idea generally attributed to positivists. And there is a certain foundation for that in the scheme of history proposed by Auguste Comte, the father of positivism. He found it necessary in the final stages of his sublime plans for remaking the world, to set forth as a basic precept, "Live for others." He thought he had scientific proof for this moral doctrine and in my own opinion he had and we have also. But this is not the same thing as saying that moral or philosophical judgments which cannot be verified scientifically are on that account always to be discarded. Perhaps in the value world, all rules of scientific thinking, except the law of *parsimony*, will prevail.

For our purposes, here, this question need not be finally answered. It is not my thesis that rigorous thinking is always and only scientific, since it was the philosophers who established logic. And still less is it said here that this scientific method will suffice to cure all the ills of society or that it should be the exclusive occupation of statesmen and teachers. The proposition is more modest; it is only that scientific or objective thinking is what we now need most. And that making it a more general habit among men is not impossible.

The relation between scientific and value judgments that needs to be affirmed, when authoritarian philosophers and pseudo-scientists ask questions, is this: They support each other. It is a basic principle in the educational philosophy of John Dewey that the world would be benefited by a wider and more thorough application of the scientific method. We are here advocating one of Dewey's most fundamental ideas. Not that he invented it; indeed it has been endemic in social philosophers since men began to reason about their affairs. But it is worthwhile to note Dewey's solid and persuasive urging of this principle because there are so many who speak, first, as if it were new; second, as if it had recently been thoroughly tried; third, as if the time had come for something else since the scientific method has not brought desired results. This reasoning, we may be bold enough to say, is only the recurrent resistance of man to those better elements in his own nature that will in the end completely civilize him.

Authoritarian objections to giving men the tools of free thought do not, however, come only from stubbornness and certainly not from stupidity. The intellect can be ranged against science, as many working men of the laboratories have discovered to their sorrow and surprise. The seventeenth-century turn toward experiment and testing by the senses became, in Whitehead's words, an "anti-intellectualist" movement because it was a turn from subtle and elaborate structures of the logical imagination toward the simple manipulation of things. So today brilliant minds can fool themselves with intricate symbolic patterns which take them so far from sensory experience that they can believe they have reached a world where the senses do not count. Resistance to the furtherance of scientific thought exists today in centers of great learning and among very learned men.

We have, as it has often happened before, the spectacle of some of the most thoughtful of men joining, on intellectual grounds, in trying to persuade other men not to think in the way here proposed. This is partly a reborn authoritarianism in American thought. It follows the second element against us, which is the revolutionary philosophy of Europe, especially in the Fascist states. It adds to and encourages the first element of opposition, which is man's lazy nature, the inertia of the mind.

The intellectualist movement against science has two phases, and one does not find the same men speaking in both camps; indeed they would probably deny with some heat that they are fighting on the same side. There are the authoritarians. They call themselves by various names. They unite in denying that man can get at any viable truth by his own efforts. Second are those who arrive at their mistrust of science by a different path. They have misread and misused the findings of science itself to discredit thought about human affairs.

We can look at these pseudo-scientists for a moment. Probably Xenophanes was not the first to point out that the gods are made by man in his own image. He said, you'll remember, that if the lions and the oxen could worship they would burn sacrifices to gods that looked like lions and oxen. That is one of the first of a long series of statements declaring that all ideas belong in a frame of reference, but probably others were ahead of Xenophanes, even in western philosophy. Students today, who read casually the works of sociologists of knowledge like Karl Mannheim, or of "positive" sociologists like Pareto, can sometimes be caught speaking as if the discovery of the relativity of opinion, of the fact that our thinking about human affairs is colored by our interests, were something quite new. It might be shown, but cannot here be proved, that both instrumentalism in philosophy and the Gestalt movement in psychology have contributed to this mistaken notion and still more to the serious blunder that it leads to, namely, the idea that because all thinking has a background and is affected by interests, there is no use in trying to think objectively about human problems.

We are not accusing Dewey of this, of course, nor Wertheimer and Koffka. Even Karl Marx is less guilty than some critics have made him out to be. The disciples of original thinkers de-

77

velop both the absurdities and the poisons that are contained in all systems of thought. But it is perfectly evident that there is a diseased form of instrumentalism current among us that says something like this: "We know that all men's thoughts about human affairs are rooted in their practical desires. Nobody can think independent of his purposes. Hence, because we cannot really reach the ideal objectivity and truthful detachment that the old logicians advised, there is no use trying. We should believe whatever is most in agreement with the purposes we are working for." If they had a slogan maker like Goebbels, he would say for them, "We will think with the will!"

This "making a virtue out of a difficulty" may be more widespread among political and literary people than it is among educators. It is a kind of half-articulated creed with some of them, how many one could not say. In any case, it is dangerous because it has a root in science, because it is a perversion of scientific thinking rather than a direct attack upon it.

Frank and simple believers in authority are hard to find. I will name no names, and if no one arises to say he has been attacked, it is possible that I shall be proved completely mistaken. And the reason for thus avoiding the direct accusation is that this tendency masquerades as several other things. It betrays itself sometimes in declaring that someone—like Dewey, for example—wants to make all judgments scientific or wants to deny that there are any values beyond the reach of laboratory techniques. Dewey can defend himself as he pleases; I am concerned only to observe the event. Whenever anyone accuses a teacher of trying to make "everything scientific," adding that "many judgments are better made on other premises and other ways," watch him! He probably, for some reason, thinks science has already found out too much, and he is afraid of what it may go on to discover.

However expressed, there is a widespread desire to restore authority as a masterful factor in our intellectual life. This question is subtle and complex. I shall immediately be suspected of denying that authority has any place at all, which is far from my opinion. But men have a natural tendency to lean back upon authority. The intellectual balance of any time is precarious. It is not likely ever to lean too far away from authority. It will, if we can judge by human behavior in the past, lean almost always backward toward authority. And for the most part that balance will be against any change, no matter how desirable. Authority is by its nature conservative; it is an enemy of the spirit of free inquiry. There may come a time when we shall be justified in saying that our intellectual life lacks the salutary amount of respect for achieved knowledge and experienced judgment. I cannot find that it has ever happened up to now. And I am sure that we are not now in any such epoch of general recklessness of mind.

There are persons all about us, of course, who show almost no respect for any value. But these persons do not share in the life of the mind; nor will a restoration of a mild inquisition touch them in any way. It is precisely for the purpose of bringing clear thought and knowledge to them that we are urging our enterprise. The kind of authority I am decrying stands in the way because it says to them: The life of the mind is only for those who can suffer the proper initiation. There is only one road. No arduous or earnest travel on any other will get you anywhere at all.

Take, for example, our current excitement about the "best books." This interest, of which we have always had recurring flashes at fairly regular intervals, has been exploited by publishers and publicists and has also been the focus of some valuable educational experiments. We have no way of knowing whether or not those most concerned with causing the present stir wished to reinstitute or encourage the worship of authority in literary and philosophical judgments. They may not have desired to put new glamour on submission. But whatever their intention, that was the effect on many readers. These readers were being told not only what to read but how to read it. Nothing further was required but to work hard in the ways of the master. Their disappointments are not a necessary part of our present record. Their pathetic response to an old method, long since outgrown, is more important. And there are certainly those

81

who watch for these public weaknesses to set up once again restrictions and impediments upon intelligence.

Contrary to this ancient dogmatism, science is not dogma. The method evolves and changes by self-correction. It is less comforting because it asks us to try to create our own wisdom. But it is more dependable, and it is our protection against enslavement as well as against mistakes.

V

SCIENCE FOR MEN, NOT MASTERS

This brief essay is not a manifesto. It does not end in a slogan, nor even in a practical program. The ways in which these great purposes are to be attained are not altogether clear, and to devise them will take the best brains and greatest skills that we possess. The first step is to regain our faith in reason, which is an old virtue often lost, and to add to it something more recent, the faith in science as a means of controlling nature for secular intentions. To control nature we must begin by knowing natural things. As Thorndike, who has helped so much toward such a purpose, says, "The twentieth century has discovered a new virtue, that of facing the realities of nature." [1] A new virtue, very

[1] E. L. Thorndike, *Human Nature and the Social Order* (Macmillan, 1940), p. 390.

difficult to reach up to and hard to live by. To do that we shall have to learn to be new men. But nature, the secular sensible world, can be controlled in no other way.

We know a few of the things we have to do. We must give not only freedom but also support to agencies and institutions in which thought is possible. Here again we must beware of complacency. We are proud of them, but the support we give our libraries and colleges, our laboratories and research enterprises, is none too generous and is likely, unless other fundamental aims can be accomplished, to grow less.

These institutions, the source of any possible progress, are in danger. We can see the obvious danger of political interference. Look abroad. What is happening to free and fruitful investigation in Russia is a much debated question on which I am not in a position to have an opinion. But if Communism, as practiced today, is a form of totalitarianism that cherishes scientific truth, Russia differs in that respect from the other monolithic states. Most of all, of course, from Germany, for the Germans have themselves told us what they are doing. The Nazis have a use for laboratories and scientific workers to strengthen their people and to make their armies more destructive. It is notable and perhaps somewhat ironic that their weapons are nearly all inventions of the democratic countries against which they are being used. But of science as a free instrument for seeking truth, there is none in Germany now and no public or private support is possible for it.

What has that to do with us? We are in conflict with the ideas of the Nazis. Perhaps we can carry on this fight without too much sacrifice of our own freedom. But their ideas must affect ours. A world in which politics is a bloody struggle abroad and a suspicious and feverish patriotism at home is not likely to have much sympathy for science. In such a state, politics must inevitably work against the use of money for free investigation. The great bulk of public expenditures for scientific work in such a time must go for devices of destruction that may defeat an enemy but can build nothing afterward. And besides, as has been pointed out by Bernal, when governments learn things in their war researches, they do not make them public and one of the first uses of science is denied; the new research adds nothing to general public knowledge.

The war may be a frightful but quite brief episode, but depressions and the evolution of capitalistic industrialism and many other forces are bringing changes that will not be transitory. For about one hundred years, since the beginning of free public schools in this country, we have been steadily dividing up by political means, among all the people, larger and larger shares of the national wealth. In my own opinion, this is a change that works generally for good. It may have been going too fast, although reformers whose zeal is more notable than their knowledge of the facts seem unaware of its happening at all. Or it may have been going too slowly; men who once get their hands on money in any amounts, small or large, can squeal when it is taken away for public uses. These questions are of immense importance but not in our province at the moment. The fact is simply that conditions, including government policies, appear to be reducing the chances of future great fortunes and hence the chances of great foundations and philanthropies, and hence by uncomfortable logic we can expect the ultimate reduction of all private scientific agencies of all kinds whatsoever. It seems quite likely that the private colleges, libraries, universities, and laboratories which survive the next few generations will do so by some kind of direct service, perhaps to business. It is not likely that benefactors will, as in the past, hand over large endowments and tell them to do what they please. It will be worse then for most private agencies; many of them may not survive at all.

That leaves scientific investigation in the hands of government itself and of the public universities and laboratories. Government research, like all other human institutions, has both virtues and faults. A great deal of the most distinguished work done in this country has been done in the laboratories of state universities and land-grant colleges. It is only accurate to point out, however, that free investigation in problems which interest the scientist because of their theoretical importance, and whose practical application is remote and uncertain, do not get from

87

legislatures and public boards the same kind of enthusiastic help that is given to more tangible dividend-paying operations.

This does not have to be so. But it is not a problem by itself. It will be solved very largely in terms of our solution of the problem of getting the general run of our citizenry, the average men and women, both to understand and practice in their own affairs the scientist's way of looking at facts.

We begin this process, of course, by doing what we can in the schools. We build them up, because whatever most of our citizens lack will be what they did not get the basis for in the schools and what they have will be what the schools have started them in. We must train all those who are capable of thinking objectively to do so, and we must teach them to be loyal to those ways of thinking. If there really are any who cannot even get a glimpse of this, they must be trained to be loyal to the society that is the creation of the gifted.

We can support the institutions of science, however, and develop the public schools, and still be far short of success. The reasons for this are the familiar reasons offered for what we call adult education. No schooling in the first few years of life can equip a child to be a man or woman of a modern world. Learning must go on. We are beginning to take that for granted. At least, leaders take it for granted and plan for it. The schools can make a foundation, and science can go on, but for men and women living the diurnal round of the world's work there must be interpretation. The world that men learned a little about when they had their brief schooling changes day by day. It must be studied constantly or it becomes obscure and difficult. We can, we hope, establish habits in the young that will make continuous learning and clear thinking possible. We can make them into citizens proud of intelligence and ashamed of the passionate follies that have passed, in most of history, for great action. Such habits will make it difficult to cow them by authority. But if the medicine men continue to balk interpretation, if what is learned by the great has no meaning for the rest of us, we are still not succeeding. We must produce and use Arnold's "true men of culture." We need what James Harvey Robinson began to ask for nearly twenty years ago, a "humanizing of knowledge."

One need is quite specific. We need to teach our people to be readers of books. Not only readers of the books that now stand idle on the shelves of homes and libraries. Many of these have meat in them, of course, and they will be read again sometime not only by a few but by multitudes. In the meantime, we need to get men to think of reading as an expression of their own needs and purposes. We need a functional idea of reading so that men will turn naturally to books as tools for their own purposes.

We speak of education as the organization of the ways of taking advantage of the experience of others. For this books have a primary usefulness. Not books alone. Not reading alone. Listening, watching, experimenting—the communication of ideas by every medium. All are needed. But books have a special place.

Why books? Why not encourage the daily newspaper habit and hope that this will lead in time from those papers that are printed for people who cannot read to those printed for people who can? Why not pray that looking at pictures and perusing the captions only when necessary, which is seldom, will in good time lead to a taste for solid pages of type? Or why not, indeed, admit that newspapers and magazines are very good reading in themselves and call the use of books only a stuffy academic habit best forgotten in a modern world? There are some who appear to believe that you cannot fit a bookshelf into a streamlined design.

The answer is not mere superstition. Newspapers and magazines have their uses. They are not the uses of books. The chief reason for this is that newspapers, and in only a slightly lesser degree the magazines, are not in the business of giving you systematic and reasoned accounts of any subject. They will not sell knowledge or understanding; they sell news. The difference between knowledge and news may not be evident at first thought to the reader, but we can be quite sure that a newspaper editor knows the difference. If he did not he would soon be earning his living otherwise.

The test is this. Can you imagine preferring yesterday's newspaper to today's? Why not? Obviously because every paper that comes out is shrewdly put together to make you think its content, perforce made up of what has happened or transpired within twelve hours or so, is more important than anything that has happened for days and days. It appeals to us because it is freshly new; not for any other reason. The newspaper editor prints what his staff can find out, and we can admire wholeheartedly their skill and patience and energy in getting it for our enjoyment. He dresses it up to make it seem as important as possible, not in the proportions of its real importance in any whole scheme of things, not in relation to a subject or a philosophy or even a focused human need. It is offered as the latest discoverable, almost true, thing that can be told.

Without this marvelously adept and devoted service to our hungry minds we could not live in the world. It is a tragic and ugly world, but we have to look daily on its distorted face. That is not, however, the way to learn in due proportion and degree to understand basic scientific ideas, philosophic systems of value, to learn one's way around in politics or art or drama or music. Some magazines, to be sure, are more like books. In that case, they are books. We treat them and keep them as such.

There are similar handicaps in using any other medium of communication or any other method of presentation. We can go out of the world of print altogether. The museum is an instrument of general education whose possibilities we are only now beginning to appreciate. But the things that a museum can teach are still limited, and there are few real museums in the country, and most people go into museums much more rarely even than they sit down to read a book.

The radio is, or someday is going to be, the greatest instrument for the development of popular taste that we have thus far created. Those who have spent years in experimenting with its possibilities know that it still has miraculous things to do. But the radio is an approach to the mind that works only by slow changes, and its cumulative effect is in standards, not in knowledge. We can use it to excite, and we can use it for certain kinds of news, still more ephemeral than that we get from the newspapers. It gives also a kind of direct experience. But you cannot present systematic and exhaustive accounts of serious subjects on the air to the general public, at least not by any methods now in use, because you cannot ever count on any hearer's ever having heard the broadcasts that went before. He insists on the sampler's privilege of tuning in on any program at any time and getting his time's worth. He will not patiently be told that he must listen today if he would understand tomorrow, or, worse, that he can't expect to understand what is going on at the moment because he has not followed the thirteen weeks' series from the start. Let us use the radio also for what it can do, and we shall discover many things undreamed of now. It is not likely that the need for books will be less on that account.

When we have admitted the need for books, and have a full realization of the fact that these interpreter's books are of a new kind and call for new skills and new materials, then we face technical problems of great difficulty. To get the history of these, we can again go back to Lord Brougham and his Society for the Diffusion of Useful Knowledge. For more than a century experiments have been going on. Mostly they have failed. We are perhaps beginning to see how the books should be written. We are still far short of any machinery by which to get the books into the hands of those who want them, as I mentioned before when we were speaking of complacency.

I have mentioned only a few of the ways in which thinking is balked for lack of knowledge There are many more. These problems, however, are only problems; they are not traits of the natural world that we have to accept with resignation. If the desire to solve them could be roused to a pitch that would make this only one of the faintest of our national interests, that would be enough. They would be solved.

The ultimate question is always, what kind of civilization do we want? There is more than one measure of the good life. A well-known scholar remarked in a broadcast conversation a few months ago that a period in civilization should be judged by its fruits. "Take for example," he said, or words to this effect, "the Thirty Years' War. That period from 1618 to 1648 is often spoken of as miserable. The common citizen of the time had pretty bad going. But in that period there flourished in Europe such men as John Milton, Descartes, and others who left us great treasures. Can such a period be called a period of failure?" He could have gone on and named Bacon, Spinoza, Comenius, Galileo, Hobbes, Locke, Pascal, and others, because they all flourished in those black destructive years. No, we cannot say that such a period was a failure. But, on the other hand, can we by any humane and reasonable definition of civilization call it a success?

This is a question worth considering. In the first place, none of these men had much effect on the lives of their immediate contemporaries, unless you think that some poor driven peasant, fleeing death through the mud and rubble that had been once a town, stopped to thank God that he lived at the same time as Blaise Pascal or Thomas Hobbes. We are the ones who can be benefited now, in the safety of centuries after, by the *Pensées* or the *Leviathan*.

In the second place, was the existence or the greatness of any of these men a result of which thirty years of horror were a cause? I do not think so. It seems more likely that something else than misery made greatness. A generation of senseless killing not only did not make great poets but must have made many inglorious Miltons mute.

There is plenty to show that greatness comes at all times. But great thought does not seem to come only out of human follies or catastrophe. It is true that Plato and Aristotle came out of a Greek culture that was falling apart. So Montaigne and Bodin, that French half-Plato, lived in the muck of French religious wars, and Goethe went serenely, even disdainfully, about his business while German boys were dying at Napoleon's guns.

How can any time be called a success if the lives led by the people were full of cruelty and fear? It is pleasant for us to enjoy the spectacle of history as long as too much history is not exploding about our heads. But there is no time for any man to live in but his own. The successful civilization is not, then, the culture or the time that produces great men for those of after ages to enjoy. A successful moment in history is the one that makes a decent, reasonable, good life possible for all contemporaries. By this high

97

standard, successes in history have been very few.

It is well to love excellent men, but it is well also to love excellence in all human beings. These are not quite the same thing.

The first says, "I will honor those men and women who show greatness in a measure that commands my reverence."

The other says, "I will love excellence in any degree, wherever I can find it, and I will love and work for those circumstances in which all men can show whatever excellence they have."

I cannot see that it is for the good of civilization to take those things which are the expression of life as more important than life itself. We can take art very seriously, but we might still rather wish that the art critics of Vienna had made a great mistake and praised the water colors of Adolph Schickelgruber. If they had contented his vanity, the water colors might have been soon forgotten and there would have been no Hitler to murder Europe. We cannot blame those critics for not being prophets. But the moral is still there.

We know today that the fate of civilization

hangs not only on what men think but also on what they hate and what they love. We are still in danger of making one central and tragic mistake. We are in danger of going on in the mistaken belief that if men feel deeply they must feel blindly. Because emotion and prejudice have often been twins, we still think that emotion cannot be served by intelligence. Forgetting all subtle and difficult metaphysics here, because such distinctions are not what most men can live by, we may still say that education has failed to tie men's loyalties to the only kind of freedom that is worth having, the freedom to use the mind in all its untrammeled strength and to abide by clearly seen conclusions.

This is not an idea that can be easily put into practice; indeed it is not readily grasped, so murkily have we thought for generations about the relation between feeling and thought. What I am saying is that man lives by his loyalties and that if he is to live in freedom he must be loyal to freedom, and that means loyalty not to the blood but to the brain.

These corporeal metaphors do not help much. I would rather say that we must take as the basic work of education to teach men not to be afraid to think, still more to be shamed by their own failure to think, and eternally jealous of anything that would deny them the right to follow where intelligence leads. The life of freedom is the only possible condition in which thinking can be fertile and useful to happiness. Reason can establish, moreover, that a free life is more than merely the kind of life that is compatible with free thought. It is, as proved by reason, the best life. This is not prejudice—or, at least, I am not resting the case on prejudice. The case rests on the clearest thinking men have ever been capable of.

To establish such a difficult point is beyond the scope of this brief discussion. The present task is different. It is to urge a new kind of character training, a new kind of morality, if you will, upon our teachers and ourselves. Perhaps we can make this more concrete by listing some of the things that the word "Freedom" stands for in the minds of different men. For some, it is no doubt just a word, a lovely sound, and they are so easily enchanted by it that anyone who sings it can lead them anywhere he will. Such men can be enslaved and can even be happy for a time, devoting their humanity to lies. But we have nothing to do with this meaningless use of the word, nor indeed with any ambiguous uses that can lead to tragedy.

To some, the word freedom means the right to use one's own strength to build up a position of power—in government, in social influence, in finance, in intellectual prestige. Such persons can be understood; in some instances they can even be useful if they earn their eminence by doing things that are intrinsically valuable. But this is not the highest and best meaning of the word.

In its highest and best meaning, the word freedom is bound to the word responsibility. It is more than freedom *from* something; it is freedom *for* something. It is freedom to act but to act with the greatest form of human energy, and the greatest form of human energy is the use of the mind to solve the problems of human good.

Man is judge of his own destiny, and he is not making mean use of his mind if he applies it to the search for his own happiness. Everything but intelligence has been tried heretofore to discover how men can be happy. They have not often been certain of what they wanted and still less often successful in getting it. Men need not even feel that they are lacking in religious deference to the Universe if they fix attention on their own secular destiny. The evidence that this rationality would interfere with moral salvation is not impressive.

It is a serious mistake to suppose that the importance of thought is a function of its subject matter, as when the theologians say that the greatest thinking must by its nature be thinking on the nature of God. The power of a creator would be shown in anything he created, and in the same way the power of thought is not conditioned by its problems but by its own quality. Science is not less than other thinking because it is thinking about nature. Nature is the manifestation of reality, and if we could find out what reality is, one suspects that we would find the essence of all reality in the reality of anything.

"Man's chief good," said Aristotle, "is in energy of the soul according to the best and most perfect virtue." This energy is thought and the use of knowledge. The highest energy of man is to solve his own problems on all levels, in view of all purposes, with his highest gift, which is thought controlled by nothing but its own essential powers.

It is difficult to understand how anyone can read history and still believe that men get into earthly trouble because of mere lack of convictions, or even for lack of convictions morally sound. Socrates was right; men mostly do what they think is good. The crimes of men and the follies of nations are the result. It is not their disregarded consciences but their mistakes that destroy them. What they need, we insist, is more knowledge and straighter thinking about consequences of what they do. It is a pitiful illusion that good motives ever kept a man from the consequences of a bad error. To take but one example, how many babies have died because their mothers, in selfless and anxious ignorance, did what was certain to kill them?

Not only the desire to do well in this world —we need that, but it is not enough. There must be also the knowledge of what to do. And a love of whatever makes that knowledge possible.

Men have always tried to influence each other. Poets and teachers, preachers, statesmen, saints and demagogues—they have all tried to persuade men to change their behavior and their characteristic selves. This is obvious, and for the most part we are not alarmed by the fact that we are subject all through our lives to the deliberate attempts of other people to make us behave as they think we should. One suspects that our indifference to all but the basic schooling process is caused by our belief that most of this general propaganda is wasted. It is too ineffective. We forgive poets and demagogues for trying to make us over because they generally fail.

In the future, however, we can expect that our methods of controlling each other and ourselves will become efficient. Says Thorndike: [1] "In proportion as we treat the world as regular and resistant to outside influences we influence it. If science in the next hundred years should describe the ways of human nature and behavior as accurately as it has by now described the nature and behavior of the planets and stars, so

[1] E. L. Thorndike, *op. cit.*

that man could predict what men would do as he now predicts eclipses, he would increase his power to control the fate of men. . . . The more the world is determined, the more man can work his will upon it."

Whose will? In whose hands will be this intimate and controlling knowledge that will determine man's fate? The threat to man's freedom that lies in this growth of knowledge is fearfully shadowed in the triumph of pseudoscience over the souls of the great German people. In the right hands, knowledge of how to manage men will make for freedom and happiness. The Fascist answer to this problem is that there must be a leader who holds supremacy by telling men what to think and so handling their environment that they are moved to consent. The democratic answer is that this knowledge, like all the other goods of civilization, must not be the possession of any group of men but must be the common property of all.

The alternatives are clear. If we do not press ahead in the acquisition of knowledge of ourselves, if we refuse to use our brains to get an understanding of our own human nature as a part of the natural world we have come to know and in great measure to control, we are condemning ourselves to the slavery of unnecessary ignorance, to fumbling and recurring mistakes. If we develop a knowledge of the facts of human nature, however, and they are known only to a few, we shall be slaves to those few. There is no argument in history nor in logic that can make us believe that such power would be used for the good of all of us. If the knowledge is accessible to every man, each can then make as much use of it as his capacity will allow.

Still more, an understanding of the method, of the way in which the knowledge is being constantly built up and corrected by experience, and finally an understanding of the engineering techniques by which the knowledge is put to use must also be accessible to everyone. Then each will have the chance to benefit himself and do his part in the actual creation of the common good.

This new Promethean enterprise is more than just giving fire to men. Fire is dangerous unless men know how to use it. This enterprise is to give men both power and the knowledge of its possible uses for their good. It is to help them from suffering at the hands of those who have knowledge and would use it against them. It is to give common ownership to effective thought and also to the knowledge of what there is in the world worth having, including freedom and how to keep it. The teacher is the friend who makes men free.